WRITING ACROSS THE CURRICULUM

Written by **Beryl Bennett**

Illustrated by **Quentin Eckman**

Edited by Dianne Draze

ISBN 931724-77-5

Published by **Dandy Lion Publications**
      P.O. Box 190
      San Luis Obispo, CA

Contents

Information for the Instructor

Why teach writing in all curricular areas?

Writing is communicating. It is a way to express ourselves and to clarify our thoughts. It forces us to think ideas through in a clear and coherent way. It helps us to differentiate between what we know and understand and what still needs to be clarified. When we write, we understand the material better and remember it longer. Writing helps us integrate new ideas with old ones and formulate new questions. In other words, writing forces us to think, to analyze, to synthesize and to organize. Because of these qualities, writing is one of the most valuable skills in education.

Since the mid-1970s, researchers have repeatedly pointed out a decline in the ability of students to write well. One reason given is that students are not asked to write often enough. A logical solution, then, would be to give students more opportunities to write; to make writing an integral part of learning in all subject areas. Besides giving students more writing experiences providing them with the opportunity to write in different subject areas gives them a wider range of writing topics. Assigning writing topics that progress logically from the material being studied or from the student's actual experiences elicits better results than those topics assigned with no curriculum context.

If student writing is to improve, it can no longer be confined to the English department. Students must write often in order to learn to write well. Writing in all areas of the curriculum can provide students with the practice they need to become better writers. Teachers can benefit as well. They can have the satisfaction of knowing that their students understand the material they are presenting better and will remember it longer.

Types of writing

There are several different types of writing styles. The most common types are report of information, evaluation, problem solution, autobiographical incident, first-hand biography, observation, story, and analysis. This book presents opportunities to do two different types of writing. These two are *report of information* and *problem solution*. They are described as follows:

Report of Information - In this type of writing the writer collects data, facts, and information either from authoritative sources or first-hand observation of the given topic and presents the best of this information.

Problem Solution - In this type of writing, writers describe and pose solutions to a problem. The students may be asked to present arguments for the solution they have chosen or that has been described in the writing situation.

About this book

This book provides teachers of social science, language arts, science, math, and art with complete writing lessons for two types of writing — problem solution and report of information. The writing lessons are designed to progress logically from the material being studied in each subject area. However, if you wish to present the writing lesson and are not currently studying the selected topic, the background information provided in each lesson is sufficient to give the students all the information they need to be able to write the required assignment even if they have not studied the topic. The writing lessons are designed for 7th and 8th grade students and high ability 5th and 6th graders.

The teacher is provided with a step-by-step procedure to follow in each lesson and all the materials for conducting a successful writing lesson. The lessons guide students through the writing process by presenting the following for each lesson:

- explicit writing prompts
- pre-writing activities and information
- pre-composing sheets
- concise directions outlining the format of their writing
- checklists to guide peer editing

When these materials are presented to students in the manner outlined on the procedure page, students will know exactly what they are to write about and have a clear path to follow. The result will be writing that is clear, meets the intended goal, and is organized.

In addition to the reproducible materials that are presented to guide student's thoughts and writings, this book contains materials directed to the instructor. Each sections begins with an explanation of the type of writing (report of information or problem solution) that students will be doing. Additionally, instructors are given an outline of what procedure is to be followed when presenting the lessons, suggestions for student and teacher evaluation, guidelines for scoring, and additional writing suggestions for each subject area.

Lesson Model

Introduce → Pre-writing → Pre- → Writing → Peer → Rewriting → Evaluation
Writing   Activities   Composing   Critiquing

The model that is presented for each lesson in this book can be used to create your own writing lessons or to use with the additional writing topics supplied at the end of each section. The format presented is in general:

1. **Introduce the type of writing** - Discuss the type of writing students will be doing.

2. **Introduce the writing situation** - Read and discuss the writing prompt.

3. **Pre-writing activities** - Discuss ideas related to the writing situation and present other materials or activities related to the writing topic.

4. **Pre-composing** - Discuss the final format of the assignment and have students use a pre-composing sheet to organize their thoughts.

5. **Writing** - Have students write their first drafts.

6. **Peer Critiquing** - Have students work together to edit each other's papers.

7. **Rewriting** - Have students correct their papers and write a final draft.

8. **Evaluation** - Evaluate papers.

Writing Prompts

When planning a trip, one looks at a map for directions to the desired destination. A prompt, like a map, gives students the information they need to point them in the right direction to write. Many teachers experience disappointment when they read the final drafts of a writing assignment because their students have totally missed the intent of the assignment. A closer look often reveals that the directions for writing were not explicit; students had no map to guide them. A well written prompt can insure better results as well as relieve some of the students' anxieties about writing. Students need to know the answers to the following questions before they can begin to write. A good prompt will answer these questions; and the more specifically it does, the better the writing results will be.

- Who will my audience be?
- What am I to write about?
- What is the main purpose of the writing?
- What form should I use?

Prompts are usually written in two parts. The first part, called the writing situation gives the student background information about the assignment. The second part, the directions for writing, provides the student with the following information:

- Who the audience is — their teacher, a friend, a parent or member of the community
- The form of the writing — an essay, a letter or story
- The purpose of the writing — to relate an incident, to inform or to evaluate
- What to include in the writing — reasons or arguments, vivid verbs or adjectives, dialogue

Pre-writing Activities

The pre-writing activities are exercises that help students relate to the writing assignment or give them needed information. There are a wide range of activities that you can use to give additional information, present a relevant point of view, spur students' thinking, and urge personal involvement. You can present excerpts from stories, poems, diaries, or plays, as well as lists of facts. You can also ask students to take part in interviews, surveys, experiments and simulations. They can create idea clusters, collect samples, listen to recordings, watch films or videos, look at photos or prints, examine samples or take part in guided imageries.

Pre-composing Sheets

These sheets are designed to help students organize the ideas that were generated from the pre-writing activities. The pre-composing sheets help students limit the topic, specify support for their opinions, and develop a thesis or main idea for their writing.

Format Sheets

A writing prompt asks the students to put their writing in a particular form such as a letter or an essay. The format sheets direct the students toward this goal by outlining the requested format and offering suggestions for completing it.

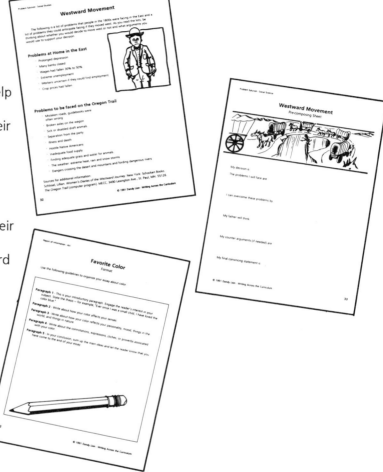

Peer Critiquing

Two sheets are provided for student use in critiquing their partner's paper. The first, the Student Response Guide, helps students to check for content to make sure all information requested in the prompt is provided in the writing. The second sheet, the Writing Checklist, covers the mechanics in the writing, spelling, punctuation, paragraphing, and grammar.

Evaluation

Evaluation is a necessary educational process that helps students recognize their strengths and weaknesses, thereby, improving future writings. Some of the ways a teacher can help create a positive attitude about writing are as follows:

1. Communicate the idea that each student has good and relevant ideas to share.

2. Provide students with many writing activities to give them the security that familiarity brings.

3. Instill confidence by finding positive things to say about each writing and by showing appreciation of it by displaying, reading and sharing it.

4. Write along with students so that they can see you enjoy writing.

The actual evaluation of writing can be done by using several methods (none of which should be used exclusively). Three techniques are using the teacher as the evaluator, peer evaluation, and oral reading.

1. The Teacher as Evaluator

It is a good idea for the teacher to be the sole evaluator at the beginning of the year to set the standards and let students know what is expected of them. Later, students should be allowed to take part in the evaluation process. It is important to note that evaluating writing is easier for the teacher if specific writing directions are given to the students when the assignment is originally made. Then the teacher knows exactly what to look for in the final draft. The following ideas may be helpful in eliminating the negative aspects of teacher evaluation.

- The students can keep their writing in a folder and select the best one from three or four writings to be turned in for teacher evaluation, thus reducing the teacher's load.

- The teacher should not correct the errors but should write specific comments that will help the students toward revising and correcting themselves. Errors may be indicated in the margin, leaving the finding and correcting of the specific errors to the student. If a paper has many errors, only a few should be indicated on a single writing. Encouraging and positive remarks must also be included.

- The teacher can concentrate on one or two aspects of a paper and grade only those chosen areas, such as content, organization, etc.

- One grade may be given for content and one for mechanics so that students will receive credit for good ideas in spite of mechanical errors.

- The teacher may use a holistic rating, looking at the writing as a whole. The grade may be a single rating for the entire piece or a set of ratings for the different features being considered. See the scoring guidelines on pages 15 and 48.

- The teacher may use writing conferences in which the student and teacher read the writing together. During the conference the teacher should concentrate on only one or two areas for improvement and offer positive reinforcement for things well done. Generally, conferences should last only a few minutes.

2. Peer Evaluating

Teachers must prepare students for peer evaluating so that they approach the activity with a supportive and encouraging attitude. The teacher should demonstrate the process with the entire class before students work in smaller groups. A highly structured format is best so that students know exactly what to do. To guide their evaluation the teacher must provide specific criteria. Holistic scoring works well for peer evaluating (see scoring guides for examples). The teacher can demonstrate the process by going over the guide with students and then reading a paper out loud, keeping it anonymous. One of the best papers should be chosen for demonstration. Discussion should follow concerning how well the writer met the criteria.

When the entire class is familiar with the process of peer evaluating, a read-around activity works well and can be done in the following way:

- Instruct students not to put their name on the final draft of their writing.

- On the due date of the final draft assign a number to each student, usually their number in the roll book. Students write the number in the right-hand corner of the final draft.

- Explain the holistic scoring guide to the class and pass out a copy to each student.

- Students, taking their own papers, get into groups of four. Groups may be chosen by the teacher or by the students.

- Pass out a slip of paper to each student to be used for score recording.

- Collect the final drafts from group one and give them to group two, collect group two's papers and give them to group three, etc. until all groups have papers to read and score. Each member of the group should have a final draft to read.

- At your signal students begin reading the paper they have. When finished they decide how well the requirements of the assignment were met according to the scoring guide and determine a score. They record the number of the paper and the score on the piece of paper provided by the teacher. They do not mark on the final draft of the paper they read.

- Signal the students to pass the paper they have read and scored to their right. They keep the piece of paper they recorded the information on. They then begin the process of reading, scoring and recording with the new paper they have received.

- When all four people have read, scored and recorded the scores from the papers in their group, collect these papers and take them to the next group.

- The process continues until each group has their original set of papers back. They do not score their group's papers.

- Collect all slips of paper used for scoring and the final draft writings.

- Record all scores given a particular paper at the top of the paper, average these scores and assign a grade for that paper.

This process takes about one 45-minute class period. Though it is time consuming, there are many benefits. Students will have had an opportunity to read all of their classmates' papers and will have been able to see the differences in style and approach. They also will have shared ideas and will have critically reviewed the papers of others.

3. Oral Reading

The evaluation process can be as simple as having the students read their papers out loud. Papers can be read just for the sharing of ideas or the teacher can elicit responses from the class. In order to guide the class's response to the oral reading, the class and teacher can devise questions to be answered by the evaluators. This procedure helps students know what types of comments are acceptable. The questions can be a simple as the following.

- What did you like about the composition?

- Was there something you did not understand?

- How could this composition be improved?

Students should have time to think about what they have heard before they are asked to respond. They should be reminded to be supportive and encouraging. Teacher comments should come after the students have had their turn to comment. Students who feel that their writing would be too embarrassing or injurious should be excused from reading.

Evaluation is necessary for writing improvement. By having a positive attitude and creating an encouraging and supportive atmosphere, teachers can help students find enjoyment in learning how to improve their writing. Students can help their teachers, too, by sharing in the process through peer evaluation.

Problem Solution Writing

In problem solution writing, the writers define or describe a problem and offer one or more solutions to it. They must convince the reader that their solutions are valid by arguing for them. Writers may use examples, facts, statistics, antidotes or definitions to support their arguments. The reader's anticipated objections may need to be addressed.

Problem Solution Writing

Main Features

Students should be familiar with the following elements of problem solution writing before they begin.

1. **The beginning** - The writer should engage the reader's interest.

2. **Stating the problem** - The writer provides sufficient information so that the reader understands the problem, its causes and effects.

3. **Proposing a solution** - In a logical, coherent manner, the writer proposes one or more solutions and gives steps for implementing them.

4. **Convincing the reader** - The writer tries to convince the reader that the proposed solutions are effective ways to proceed and provides reasons for accepting the solutions. The writer may discuss the pros and cons of the alternatives, refute counter arguments or address potential doubts and criticisms of the reader.

Lesson Model

The model that is presented for each lesson in this book can be used to create your own writing lessons or used with the additional writing topics.

1. **Introduce the type of writing** - Discuss problem solution writing and go over the main features of this type of writing.

2. **Introduce the writing situation** - Read and discuss the writing prompt. Discuss the ideas that are presented in the writing prompt.

3. **Pre-writing activities** - Discuss ideas related to the writing situation. Present other materials (excerpts from books, poems, facts, or actual activities such as experiments or surveys) related to the writing topic. Material should be selected to give students additional information or to initiate thinking about the selected topic.

4. **Pre-composing** - Discuss the final form that the writing will be in (essay, diary, letter, script, story, etc.). Have students organize their ideas, facts and arguments on a pre-composing sheet.

5. **Writing** - Have students write their first drafts.

6. **Peer Critiquing** - Assign partners and have students work together to edit each other's papers using the peer editing guides.

7. **Rewriting** - Have students use the comments from the peer editing to correct their papers and write a final draft.

8. **Evaluation** - Evaluate papers based on suggestions in the section on evaluation.

Scoring Guide for Problem Solution Writing

	6-5 A-B range	4-3 C range	2 D range	1
Effectiveness	Reader knows the purpose of the essay. Presents problem fully. Offers one or more solutions. At least one or more solutions are fully developed and consistently argued.	Reader knows the purpose of the essay. Briefly discusses the problem. The writer offers at least one moderately developed solution that is relevant to the problem.	Purpose of the essay is sketchy. Merely implies a problem. Lists solutions without developing any in full. Offers little or no argument for proposed solution.	Off the subject
Fluency, Organization, Vocabulary	Each section is developed coherently. Effective transitions between paragraphs. Strong introduction and conclusion. Fresh, descriptive and mature vocabulary.	Sections are adequately organized but extraneous details interrupt forward movement. Weak introduction and conclusion. Some variety in vocabulary but may use cliches.	At most, writer states the topic. Weak organization. Details may be irrelevant. Limited vocabulary.	
Mechanics	Capitalization, punctuation consistently done correctly. Rarely makes spelling errors.	Capitalization, punctuation consistently done correctly. May misspell difficult words.	Few correct uses of capitalization; limited use of appropriate punctuation. Frequent spelling errors of common words.	
Format	Title, margins, indentations done properly. Neatly written in ink or typed.	Title, margins, indentations done properly. Neatly written in ink or typed.	Titles, margins, indentations done properly. Paper may be messy and written in pencil.	

Save the Environment

Writing Situation

Earth has limited resources. How to protect and conserve these natural resources is a problem of vital importance to all of us living now and also for future generations. Environmental problems are numerous and may seem overwhelming at times, but they all have one thing in common; they stem from the way we live. To find solutions each of us needs to examine our own lifestyle to find ways to preserve and conserve natural resources. If we each do our part, we can make a difference.

Directions for Writing

Write an essay about the problems threatening our environment. Discuss some of the problems that result from the polluting of our environment, the destroying of our natural resources and, in general, the threatening of the lives of plants and animals (including ourselves). Begin by describing the specific problems you will be writing about. Offer solutions by describing the ways you and people your age can help to protect our environment. Be specific in your recommended solutions. End your essay by summing up the main ideas in a good conclusion.

Save the Environment
Some Environmental Problems

Here are some statements that describe some of the problems with our environment. These will give you some ideas of problems to write about in your paper. As you think of other problems, write them on the back of this piece of paper.

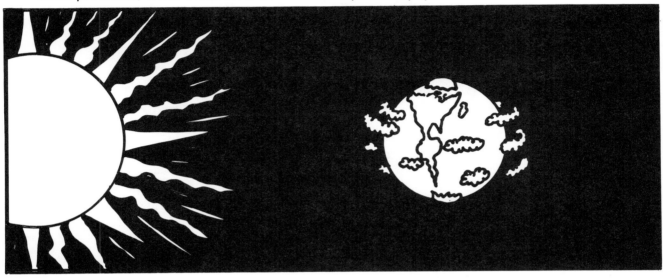

The Greenhouse Effect

"In less than two centuries, humans have increased the total amount of carbon dioxide in the atmosphere by 25% from the burning of fossil fuels and the destruction of forests. Unless we reduce emissions of greenhouse gases, the stable, hospitable climate on which civilization is based could become a thing of the past." — *Cooling the Greenhouse*, NRDC

Ozone Problems

"Ozone, the primary component of smog, is a gas formed when nitrogen oxide and hydrocarbons combine in sunlight. In the atmosphere, ozone occurs naturally as a thin layer that protects us from the sun's ultraviolet rays. But when it is formed at ground level, it's deadly." — *The Clean Air Project*

Garbage

"America has for a long time taken the cheapest option in waste disposal: 90% of its rubbish is simply dumped in landfill sites and buried. But landfill sites are filling up; a third have closed since 1980." — *The Economist*

Acid Rain

"Sulphur and nitrogen oxides, pollutants released by coal-burning electric power plants or motor vehicles, are spewed into the atmosphere. There they are changed chemically and they fall back to earth as acidified rain or snow. This destroys plant and animal life in streams, damages forests, and even erodes buildings." — *Cleaning Up The Outdoors*

Save the Environment
Interesting Facts and What You Can Do

Here are some facts related to environmental problems and also some specific suggestions of things you can do to solve some of the environmental problems facing our world.

Running Water

- A running faucet puts 3-5 gallons of water down the drain every minute it is on.

- You can easily use more than 5 gallons of water if you leave the tap running while you brush your teeth.

- Washing dishes with the tap running can use an average of 30 gallons of water.

Turn on water only when you need to. You can reduce water consumption by shortening the length of your shower and using a low-flow shower head.

Bags

- It takes one 15-20-year-old tree to make enough paper for only 700 grocery bags.

- Plastic bags often wind up in the ocean and kill marine animals that get tangled up in them or swallow them. All plastic is made from petroleum, a non-renewable source. The ink used on plastic bags contains cadmium, a toxic heavy metal. When printed plastic bags are burned, heavy metals are spewed into the air.

Save your lunch bag. Fold it up and use it another day. Use containers for your food instead of plastic bags whenever possible. Take a cloth bag with you when you shop.

Styrofoam

- Polystyrene foam is completely non-biodegradable; it just won't go away. Even 500 years from now, the foam cup you drink a soda from might still be around.

- It wastes enormous amounts of precious space at already-bulging landfills.

- Polystyrene foam is deadly to marine life. If floats on ocean surfaces, breaks up into pellets resembling food, and is consumed.

Use paper cups whenever possible. Ask fast food restaurants to use paper cups and plates. Write letters to them and ask your friends to also.

Beaches

- Taking plastic off the beach saves lives. Plastic fishing gear, bags, and other plastic wastes kill up to a million seabirds, 100,000 sea mammals, and countless fish each year.

Next time you go to the beach, take a trash bag. Spend a few minutes picking up any litter you find.

Recycling Paper

- It takes an entire forest (over 500,000 trees) to supply Americans with their Sunday newspapers every week.

Start a recycling project in your home. Stack newspapers, tie them in bundles, and take them to designated recycling centers. To save paper, write on both sides of your paper.

Glass

- The energy saved from recycling one glass bottle will light a 100-watt bulb for four hours.

Sort glass bottles according to color (clear, green and brown) and take them to a recycling center.

Aluminum

- The energy saved from one recycled aluminum can will operate a television set for three hours. Recycling aluminum cuts air pollution by 95% and means we save limited raw materials.

Rinse, crush and take aluminum cans to designated centers.

Trees

- Trees can, over time, remove large quantities of carbon dioxide (the main greenhouse gas) from the atmosphere.

Plant a tree and encourage your friends to do the same.

Save the Environment
Pre-composing Sheet

Use this sheet to organize your thoughts about some possible solutions to the problems with our environment.

List three general problems that threaten our environment.	Briefly describe the destructive effects each of these problems has on our environment.	List ways you could change your lifestyle to help alleviate the problem.
1. _____ _____ _____ _____	1. _____ _____ _____ _____	1. _____ _____ _____ _____
2. _____ _____ _____ _____	2. _____ _____ _____ _____	2. _____ _____ _____ _____
3. _____ _____ _____ _____	3. _____ _____ _____ _____	3. _____ _____ _____ _____

After you have organized your ideas, write the thesis statement you will use in your introductory paragraph.

_____, _____, and _____ are three problems that threaten our environment.

Save the Environment
Format

Use the following guidelines to organize your essay about how we can save our environment.

Paragraph 1 - This is your introductory paragraph. Write a general statement about why we need to save the environment. Make the last sentence in this paragraph your thesis statement. Fill in the blanks in the following sentence to construct your thesis statement: " _____, _____ and _____ are three problems that threaten our environment."

Paragraph 2 - Write about the first of the three problems listed in your introductory paragraph and offer solutions for what you can do to help solve the problem.

Paragraph 3 - Write about the second problem and offer solutions as to what can be done to help solve the problem.

Paragraph 4 - Write about the third problem and offer your solutions.

Paragraph 5 - Sum up your main ideas in a good conclusion. Restate the necessity of saving the environment.

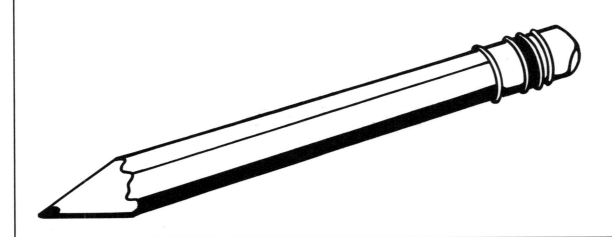

Using Fractions and Percents

Writing Situation

You have been studying fractions and percentages in your math class. Your teacher feels that students are having problems because they lack an understanding of the usefulness of this knowledge in everyday life. She feels that if the students realized the importance of fractions and percentages in everyday life, their class work would be more meaningful and they would do a better job. Your problem is to convince your teacher that you understand the many ways this information is useful to you, not only at your present age, but also in the future.

Directions for Writing

Write an essay for your math teacher. Convince her that you understand the importance of knowing fractions and percentages by giving examples of their use in everyday life. Be specific. Begin your essay with an introductory sentence and conclude it with a statement that sums up the main ideas.

Using Fractions and Percents

The Fraction Dilemma

by Beryl Bennett

If fractions are only a part of the whole,
What part are they? I'd like to know!
If I can have only a fraction of cake,
How big is the piece? How much can I take?
If a fraction of games were won by our team,
Are we winners or losers? Or somewhere between?
If the bike is on sale for a fraction of the cost,
How much money is saved? How much of it lost?
If a fraction of tourists are riding the train,
How many are driving? Or taking the plane?
If a fraction of people try the big spin,
How many will lose? How many will win?
Fractions need numbers for meaning, I guess,
To help us determine what's more or what's less.

Percents

by Beryl Bennett

I just heard the weatherman say,
A thirty percent chance of rain today.
The stock market made a ten percent gain,
It could climb higher tomorrow they claim.
Interest rates jumped another percent,
Lucky are those whose money is lent.
An ad arrived in yesterday's mail,
Everything's forty percent less in their sale.
Population grew five percent this year,
Is overcrowding something to fear?
Workers request a six percent raise,
They say the cost of living has risen these days.
Since percents abound in our world, it would seem,
That every wise person should know what they mean.

Using Fractions and Percents
Fascinating Facts

Here are some facts that are stated using fractions and percentages. These show some ways that fractions and percentages are used in everyday life. As you read these facts, be thinking about all the places you find fractions or percentages being used.

1. About 84% of parents now use car safety seats for their infants and toddlers — more than triple the percentage in 1981. When correctly used, child restraints reduce the risk of fatalities by an estimated 70%.

2. Each American consumes, on an average, about 133 pounds of sugar a year from all sources. That accounts for 1/5 to 1/4 of all calories consumed or about 500 to 600 calories per person per day.

3. In 1965, about 40% of the adults in the U.S. smoked and in 1987 about 29% smoked. If this trend continues, only 22% will smoke in the year 2000.

4. In 1989, 35/100 (or 35%) of high school athletes were girls, compared to only 7/100 (or 7%) in 1972.

5. Teens spent $55 million in 1988. Here are the percentages of 13 - 19 year old girls who own:

cameras	85%	stereos	70%
tape recorders	45%	tennis rackets	26%
VCR's	16%	motor scooters	12%
stocks/bonds	12%	golf clubs	5%

6. A study of Cincinnati children in September 1989, showed that 55% of the girls and 35% of the boys in all grades wanted to be thinner than they were.

7. According to a 1990 study on what children worry about, about 24% of the kids said they feel pressure to do well in school, 17% worry about what to do with their lives, 3% worry about teen suicide, 3% are troubled about violence in the school, 13% expressed concern about drug abuse and 38% feel the pressure to "fit in."

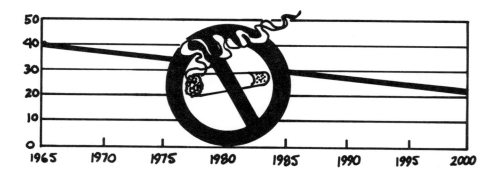

Extra Project - Cut out examples from magazines and newspapers of how percentages and fractions are used. Paste the phrases containing percentages and fractions on a piece of paper to make a collage.

Using Fractions and Percents
Pre-composing Sheet

Use this sheet to organize your ideas about how fractions and percentages are used in everyday life. The left hand column lists some general areas where you might use percentages and fractions. In the right hand column, write a specific example of how percentages or fractions might be used in this situation.

Where percentage are used

1. Discounts on sale purchases
2. Interest on money borrowed or loaned
3. Sales tax on merchandise
4. Salary or allowance increases
5. Salesperson's commission on items sold
6. Weather predictions
7. Population increases or decreases
8. Determining grades on assignments
9. Sports

Where fractions are used

10. Measuring ingredients in baking
11. Measuring yardage
12. Measuring distances
15. Room measurements
14. Your ideas _____

Your own example

1. A $75.00 tennis racket is marked down 40%
2. _____
3. _____
4. _____
5. _____
6. 50% chance of rain tomorrow
7. _____
8. _____
9. _____

10. 3/4 cup of flour
11. _____
12. _____
13. _____
14. _____

Using Fractions and Percents
Format

Use the following guidelines to organize your essay about the importance of knowing about fractions and percentages.

Paragraph 1 - This is your introductory paragraph. State the problem by saying something like, "My teacher does not think I really understand the importance of knowing fractions and percentages." Make the last sentence in this paragraph your thesis statement. Write something like, "Percents and fractions are commonly used in our everyday life."

Paragraph 2 - Write about one general area where percentages are used. For instance, begin with a topic sentence like, "We use percentages in money matters." Include at least three specific examples and explanations.

Paragraph 3 - Write about another area of everyday life where percentages are often used. Give examples of this use of fractions or percentages.

Paragraph 4 - Write about how fractions are commonly used. Your beginning sentence might be something like, "Fractions as well as percentages are commonly used everyday." Give examples and explain them.

Paragraph 5 - Conclusion. Sum up your main ideas in a sentence or two that convinces your teacher you really understand the importance of knowing percentages and fractions.

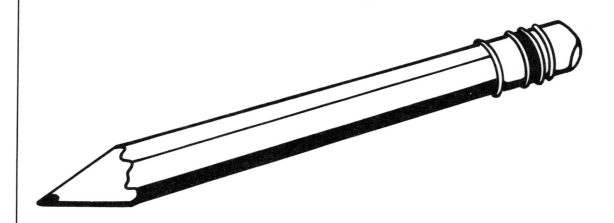

26

Dress Code

Writing Situation

Most schools have a dress code outlining appropriate clothing for students. Within the boundaries of appropriate dress at your school, you see students wearing a variety of styles. A problem arises when the popular "in" fashions include expensive brand names that many students cannot afford to buy. Imagine that your school board wants to eliminate the clothing competition by enforcing a dress code requiring all students to wear a school uniform. Would you agree or disagree with this decision? If you don't agree with the decision, what solutions would you propose for the problems presented by the pressures to dress in a certain way?

Writing Directions

Take a stand. Would you be in favor of a school uniform or against it? Write a letter to the school board giving your opinions about their school uniform policy. Give specific reasons to support your opinions. Convince them to continue or discontinue the policy. Try to overcome anticipated objections. Pose solutions to the problem other than uniforms if you don't agree that uniforms are an acceptable solution.

Dress Code

Here are some arguments that other people have voiced either to support or to refute the idea of school uniforms. As you read them, be thinking about the ideas you would like to present in your letter.

Arguments for Uniforms

1. Uniforms could cut down on clothing distractions. Students could concentrate on school subjects instead of whether they look "cool" or not.

2. Uniforms could increase students' self confidence. Students feel inferior if they don't have the right clothes.

3. Uniforms could provide students with a feeling of unity and belonging, much like the students get from team uniforms.

4. Uniforms could reduce students' clothing costs. Schools could take bulk orders and purchase uniforms at a discount.

5. Uniforms could improve classroom behavior. Clothing influences the ways students see themselves and could encourage them to live up to group standards.

6. Dress codes take time to enforce and often create hassles. Uniforms would eliminate trying to enforce a dress code.

Arguments against Uniforms

1. Requiring uniforms would be a form of harassment, trying to make students who have less power follow the rules of those in power.

2. Dressing is a way of relating to others. Limiting choices can restrict social development in school and in later life.

3. Uniforms might present an economic hardship for parents who can't afford the clothing the school requires.

4. Uniforms might be uncomfortable, especially in very hot weather. If students feel uncomfortable they are not ready to listen and learn.

5. Students need to learn how to coordinate clothing to look their best. This takes practice in making the correct choices. Getting ready for school gives students that practice.

6. The way we dress us an extension of our individual personality. Uniforms would cut out individuality and tend to make everyone the same.

Dress Code
Pre-composing Sheet

1. My thesis sentence stating whether I am for or against having school uniforms is

_____

2. My reasons are   Support for this reason

   a. _____   a. _____

     _____   _____

   b. _____   b. _____

     _____   _____

   c. _____   c. _____

     _____   _____

   d. _____   d. _____

     _____   _____

3. My opposition will probably make these objections:

_____

_____

_____

4. My arguments or alternate solutions to the clothing problem will be:

_____

_____

_____

_____

_____

_____

Dress Code
Format

Use the following guidelines to organize your letter about the school board's action requiring all students to wear uniforms.

Date

Name of school board
Address
City, State, Postal code

Dear Members of the Board;

Paragraph 1 - State your opinion of the school board's action to enforce a dress code requiring all students to wear uniforms.

Paragraph 2 - State the reasons that support your opinion. Explain each reason thoroughly.

Paragraph 3 - Overcome anticipated objections. Convince them to continue or discontinue the policy.

Paragraph 4 - If you don't agree with the school board's solution, state alternative solutions to the problem.

Paragraph 5 - Close the letter and thank them for their consideration.

Respectfully yours,
Your Name

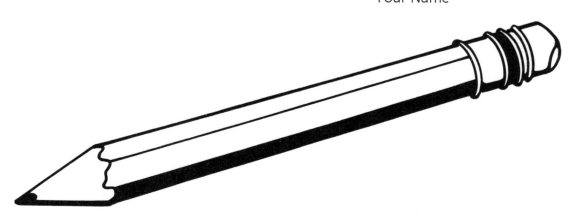

Westward Movement

Writing Situation

More than a quarter of a million Americans crossed the continental United States to Oregon between 1840 and 1870. To those hopeful, humble, hard-working emigrants from the East, the Oregon country seemed to be the promised land. Political promoters and advocates of western expansion had painted a glowing picture of a farmer's paradise of lush valleys, rivers abounding in salmon and rich lumber forests. However, to reach this distant land of "milk and honey" the emigrants had to travel the Oregon Trail — 2,000 miles over prairie, desert and mountains; 2,000 miles of misery, hunger and hardship.

Directions for Writing

You are a twenty-two year old, healthy male who is married to a healthy wife and have a two-year-old child. You live in Missouri and the year is 1841. You own a piece of land and raise wheat and corn, but the price of your crop has dropped so much you can't make a living. You have heard that Oregon is a "promised land." You know of the hardships along the trail if you go to Oregon, but you also know of the hardships facing you in Missouri. Your problem is deciding what to do — to go or to stay. Write a letter to your father telling him of your decision. Convince him you are making the right decision.

Westward Movement

The following is a list of problems that people in the 1800s were facing in the East and a list of problems they could anticipate facing if they moved west. As you read the lists, be thinking about whether you would decide to move west or not and what arguments you would use to support your decision.

Problems at home in the East

- Prolonged depression
- Many banks closed
- Wages had fallen 30% to 50%
- Extreme unemployment
- Workers uncertain if they could find employment
- Crop prices had fallen

Problems to be faced on the Oregon Trail

- Mistaken roads, guidebooks were often wrong
- Broken axles on the wagon
- Sick or disabled draft animals
- Separation from the party
- Illness and death
- Hostile Native Americans
- Inadequate food supply
- Finding adequate grass and water for animals
- The weather: extreme heat, rain and snow storms
- Dangers crossing the desert and mountains and fording dangerous rivers

Sources for additional information:
Schlissel, Lillian. *Women's Diaries of the Westward Journey.* New York: Schocken Books.
The Oregon Trail (computer program). MECC, 3490 Lexington Ave., St. Paul, MN. 55126.

Westward Movement
Pre-composing Sheet

My decision is _____

The problems I will face are _____

_____

I can overcome these problems by _____

_____

My father will think _____

_____

My counter arguments (if needed) are _____

_____

My final convincing statement is _____

_____

Westward Movement
Format

Use the following guidelines to organize your letter about your decision to stay or go on the Oregon trail.

Date, 1841

Dear Father;

Paragraph 1 - Describe your problem, state your decision and give your reasons, but save the best reason for the fourth paragraph.

Paragraph 2 - Describe the problems you will encounter if you stay or if you go. Describe how you can overcome them.

Paragraph 3 - Anticipate your father's objections and give your counter arguments.

Paragraph 4 - Give your most convincing reason for going or staying.

Paragraph 5 - In closing, ask for your father's support, approval and understanding.

Your loving son,
Your Name

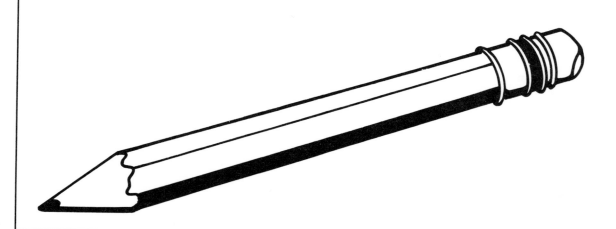

Artful Writing

Writing Situation

You enjoy drawing and doing art projects and would like to do them more often. The problem is the lack of opportunities in your school. You believe that art could be incorporated in many of your school subjects. It would help students understand the material being studied better, as well as adding enjoyment and a chance for creativity. Your problem is how to convince your teachers that it would be beneficial for them to make occasional assignments that incorporate opportunities to use art.

Directions for Writing

Write a letter to be published in your school newspaper. Address your letter to all teachers at your school. Begin by stating the problem — the lack of opportunities to incorporate art into all classes. Point out the value of doing art projects by giving specific examples for each subject area and explaining the benefits. Offer suggestions on how teachers who are not artistically inclined could become comfortable with integrating art into their classes. Be polite, specific, and convincing.

Artful Writing

Get together with a group of other students. Together brainstorm a list of ways that art could be used in all of your different classes. Use this sheet to record your ideas. Be creative and list as many ideas as possible.

_____

_____

_____

_____

_____

_____

_____

_____

_____

_____

_____

_____

_____

_____

_____

_____

_____

_____

Artful Writing
Pre-composing Sheet

Use this page to organize your ideas from your brainstorming session about the ways art could be used in your classes. Some ideas have been recorded in the left-hand column. Record your ideas in the right-hand column and continue on the back of this paper if you need more space. Select the best ideas for your essay.

1. English/Reading

   a. Draw characters in a story   d. _____

   b. Draw story's setting   e. _____

   c. Draw time line of events   f. _____

2. Social Studies

   a. Illustrate clothing of a historical period   d. _____

   b. Draw map of area being studied   e. _____

   c. Make copies of tools, homes, etc.   f. _____

3. Science

   a. Draw stages of experiments   d. _____

   b. Draw a food chain   e. _____

   c. Draw pictures of the solar system   f. _____

4. Home Economics

   a. Draw clothing designs   d. _____

   b. Draw basic food groups   e. _____

   c. Draw quilt designs   f. _____

5. Subject of your choice _____

   a. _____   d. _____

   b. _____   e. _____

   c. _____   f. _____

Artful Writing
Format

Use the following guidelines to organize your letter about providing more art opportunities in all of your subjects.

Date

Dear Teachers;

Paragraph 1 - State the problem — the lack of opportunities to do art projects in all subjects. List reasons why art projects should be included in subjects other than art.

Paragraph 2 - State your ideas for incorporating art into one of your subjects.

Paragraph 3 - State your ideas for incorporating art into another subject.

Paragraph 4 - State your ideas for incorporating art into a third area of the curriculum.

Paragraph 5 - Offer suggestions on how teachers who are not artistically inclined could become comfortable with integrating art into their classes.

Paragraph 6 - Your conclusion. Restate how students and teachers would benefit from an addition of more assigned art projects to the curriculum. Ask them to consider your proposal.

Respectfully,
Your name

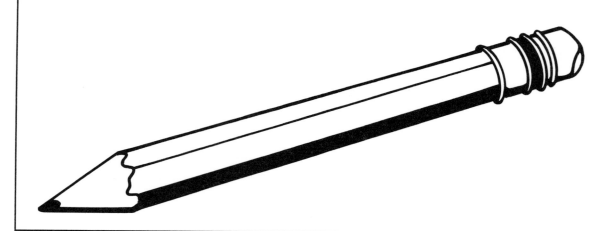

Problems with Polystyrene

Many problems exist today that result in the damaging of the earth's environment. One problem in our environment is the use of polystyrene. It is used for drinking cups and for packaging many things including hamburgers from fast-food restaurants. Gases used to make polystyrene, "eat" ozone molecules, thus depleting the ozone layer. Most polystyrene is non-biodegradable and takes up precious space at already crowded landfills. In the ocean it often breaks up into little pellets and is eaten by marine animals causing death.

Write a letter to your local fast-food restaurant asking them to replace polystyrene products with paper products. Advise them of the problems polystyrene causes to our environment. Suggest alternatives to using polystyrene. Be persuasive but polite. Use specific examples and facts.

Heart Attacks

Heart attacks are the greatest single cause of death in the United States today. Although there is no complete solution to this problem, scientists and doctors have provided guidelines for people to follow that help reduce the chances of having a heart attack.

Write an essay about heart attacks. Explain some of the ways people can reduce their chances of having a heart attack. Explain your ideas thoroughly. Sum up your main ideas in a good conclusion.

Alternate Sources of Energy

Your science class has been studying our different sources of energy. Since 1900, our use of energy has doubled every 20 years. Our supplies of fossil fuels such as coal, oil and gas are running low. One of the major problems facing all of us is how to find alternate sources of energy to meet today's needs.

Write an essay for your science teacher in which you offer possible solutions to the problem of finding alternate energy sources to fossil fuels. Convince your teacher that your ideas would work.

Money Matters

You would like to have more money to spend on extras such as tapes, movies, and snacks. Your parents cannot afford to increase your allowance. Think of ways that you could solve the problem of acquiring more spending money for yourself.

Write an essay in which you describe your problem of not having enough money for the extra things you would like to buy. In your essay specify the amount of money per week you need to enable you to buy the extras you desire. Propose thoughtful solutions to your problem. List each solution and estimate the income that could be derived from it. Be sure the income you receive adds up to the amount you said you needed at the beginning of the essay.

Budgeting Time

You want to participate in a sports program or a club activity after school that meets for two hours. The problem is that your parents do not want you to participate because they think it will interfere with your studies and chores. You feel you can solve the problem by budgeting your time wisely.

Write a letter to your parents offering solutions to the problem by outlining how you will budget your time to accomplish everything you need to do. Include the time you will arrive home, the amount of time required to do your homework and chores, and the time you will go to bed. Convince them that your plan will work.

Paying for a Project

You have a project you want to undertake. The problem is that it will cost money. You can pay for part of the expenses from your savings. Your parents might be able to help you out if you can present them with a detailed estimate of costs and good reasons for the proposed expenditures. What are some other solutions to this problem?

Write a letter to your parents outlining the project and the proposed expenditures. Estimate the cost. Explain how much you could contribute and how much you would need from them. Advise them as to how you would be able to pay them back and what interest you might be able to offer. Convince them that what you wish to do is necessary and very important to you. Try to overcome their objections with good reasons. Be specific and convincing.

Wilderness Survival

Your class has just finished reading *The Call of the Wild* by Jack London. This is a story about Buck, a gently-born, civilized dog who learned to survive in the wilderness by going back to the savage ways of his early ancestors. Buck met many obstacles and problems and learned how to overcome and solve them in order to survive.

Write an essay for your teacher. Imagine that you are Buck telling the story. Describe some of the problems you encountered and how you solved them. Be as specific as possible. Include details and feelings.

In Need of Money

Your class has just finished reading the short story, "Thank You M'am" by Langston Hughes. In this story Roger, a young boy, desperately wants a pair of blue suede shoes. His problem is he has no money and neither do his parents. He tries to solve the problem by attempting to steal the purse of Mrs. Luella Bates Washington Jones. He soon finds out he made a big mistake, but he learns a valuable lesson in the process.

Roger tries to solve his problem by stealing. Think of other ways, within the law, he could have gotten the money. Write a letter to Roger in which you acknowledge his problem and offer alternate solutions. Remember to take into account his age and circumstances. Be realistic and convince him that your ideas will work.

Conquering a Catastrophe

You have just completed a unit of study on folktales. The hero in a folktale usually has extraordinary strength or power and uses it in a conflict against overwhelming forces or obstacles. In the story "Pecos Bill: The Cyclone," Pecos Bill conquers a cyclone by riding it like a bucking bronco. Think about conflicts with other natural occurrences in nature Pecos Bill could encounter.

Write a description for a group of young children in which Pecos Bill encounters a threatening act of nature such as an earthquake or flash flood. Describe how he resolves the conflict and solves the problem. Use your imagination and include exaggeration. Remember, Pecos Bill has unlimited powers.

To Escape or Stay

Until the Civil War ended slavery in the United States, it was not uncommon for slaves to run away to the North to find freedom. The lucky ones managed to escape through the Underground Railroad. Of course, not all slaves escaped. Some were captured and taken back to their masters and punished in ways that sometimes resulted in death.

You are a twenty-year-old, healthy slave who was born and raised on a plantation in South Carolina. Your work is very hard, but your master is not exceptionally cruel. However, you have heard he is about to sell you to someone whom you know nothing about. You have also heard about a plan to escape to the North. Your problem is deciding what to do — to stay and take your chances with the new owner or to run away and take a chance on successfully finding freedom.

Write a letter to your brother who lives on a nearby plantation explaining your problem and your decision. Convince him that you are making the right decision. Anticipate his objections and provide counter arguments. End your letter with your most convincing statement.

Conducting a Campaign

You have decided to run for a student body office at your school. You really want to win, but your opponents are well-qualified and popular. What problems will you encounter in your campaign and how could you solve them? Your social studies teacher has offered to review your campaign strategy.

For your social studies teacher, write an organized step-by-step plan you can follow to organize your campaign. Identify the problems you will encounter and formulate sound resolutions.

The Boston Massacre

You are a young colonist living in Boston on March 5, 1770, the day of the Boston Massacre.

In an essay, describe the problems between the townspeople and the British soldiers as they occurred that particular day. Propose alternate solutions to those problems that could have eliminated the melee that ensued.

Three-dimensional Drawing

Artists often work on flat surfaces such as a piece of paper or a canvas, yet they do not want the objects they draw or paint to look flat. They want them to look life-like — to have dimension, to look round or solid, or to look like they move back into space. How does an artist solve the problem of creating a three-dimensional look on a flat surface?

Write an essay for your art teacher describing some of the techniques artists use to solve the problem of creating three-dimensional looking objects while working on a flat surface. Explain each example completely and the effect each particular technique accomplishes.

Art Examples

Think about the art in your school. Where are paintings displayed? Or are there any? There are many inexpensive sources where examples of good art could be obtained, yet schools are often devoid of quality examples of art work for students to view. How could this problem be solved?

Write an article for the school newspaper called "The Art in This School." In this article tell why the art in your school is not appropriate or adequate. Be sure to give specific reasons for your opinion. Tell why students should be exposed to quality art. Give suggestions as to where art work could be hung, where it could be obtained and how often it should be changed.

Gift Giving

Many holiday and special occasions occur throughout the year that involve exchanging gifts. Not having the money to buy gifts can present a problem. However, people do appreciate hand-made gifts that do not cost a lot. Thinking about the many projects you have done in art, what hand-made gift ideas could you suggest to solve the problem of wanting to give a gift and having limited funds?

Write an essay for students in your school suggesting art projects that are suitable for gifts. Describe the projects and the materials needed to make them. Convince the other students that the gifts would be appropriate and appreciated.

Student Response Guide
Checking for Content

Evaluator   _____

Author of paper _____

Title of paper _____

    This page will help your partner make sure all the elements of problem writing have been included. It will help him/her determine what should be added, changed or deleted. If you cannot answer a question, leave it blank. Your partner will know that he/she needs to clarify this point more thoroughly.

1. Does the beginning capture the reader's interest?

2. Is the problem clearly defined? Briefly state the problem.

3. Look at the proposed solution. Is it clear? What solution does the writer propose? List the reasons that support this solution.

4. Which reasons are most convincing?

5. Which reasons are the least convincing?

6. Does the voice seem appropriate for the situation? Is it consistent from beginning to end?

7. List the anticipated objections.

8. How are these anticipated objections overcome?

9. Briefly state the final convincing argument the writer gives.

10. Does the writer convince you?

11. Is there a conclusion that gives a feeling of finality?

Writing Checklist
Checking the Mechanics

Evaluator _____

Author of paper _____

Title of paper _____

This page will help your partner correct spelling errors, paragraphing, punctuation and grammar. In addition to answering the questions, your teacher may want you to use a colored pen to circle the errors on your partner's paper.

yes or no

1. _____Every sentence begins with a capital letter.

2. _____There is end punctuation for every sentence.

3. _____Paragraphing is correctly done.

4. _____Spelling has been checked (circle misspelled words).

5. _____Run-on and sentence fragments have been checked.

6. _____Sentences do not begin with "and", "so" or "so then..."

7. _____The title and all proper nouns are capitalized.

8. _____Correct punctuation (commas, contractions, etc.) is used.

9. _____Subjects and verbs agree in number.

10._____The author "shows" instead of just telling.

Comments

I especially like this about your paper. _____

_____

These things are still unclear to me. _____

_____

Report of Information Writing

In report writing the writer presents himself as an authority on a subject. After narrowing the subject to a manageable topic, the writer must characterize the information for the reader by supporting statements with facts, examples, explanations, details or anecdotes from personal experiences. Students may use their own experiences, observations and expertise and well as secondary sources of information. The writing should have a controlling idea or focus that organizes it coherently in ways such as chronologically, spatially or categorically.

Report of Information Writing

Main Features

1. **Beginning** - The writer engages the reader's interest.

2. **Controlling Idea** - The writer selects a general subject, narrows it to a manageable topic and develops a thesis or focus that will help to organize the information.

3. **Organization** - The writer organizes the information in some coherent way such as chronologically, spatially or categorically.

4. **Elaboration** - The writer develops the composition by providing evidence and/or details. This support can take the form of facts, examples, explanations, details, or personal experiences.

5. **Ending** - The writer sums up the main ideas and gives the reader the feeling that he has come to the end of the composition.

Lesson Model

The model that is presented for each lesson in this book can be used to create your own writing lesson or used with the additional writing topics supplied at the end of each section. The format in general is:

1. **Introduce the type of writing** - Discuss report of information writing and go over the main features of this type of writing.

2. **Introduce the writing situation** - Read and discuss the writing prompt. Discuss the ideas that are presented in the writing prompt.

3. **Pre-writing activities** - Discuss ideas related to the writing situation. Present the materials (excerpts from books or poems, facts, or actual activities such as experiments or surveys) related to the writing topic. Material will vary from one situation to another but should be selected to give students additional information or to start them thinking about the selected topic.

4. **Pre-composing** - Discuss the final form that the writing will be in (essay, letter, script, story, etc.). Have students organize their ideas on the pre-composing sheet.

5. **Writing** - Have students write their first draft.

6. **Peer critiquing** - Assign partners and have students work together to edit each other's papers using the peer editing guides.

7. **Rewriting** - Have students use the comments from the peer editing to correct their papers and write a final draft.

8. **Evaluation** - Evaluate papers based on suggestions in the section on evaluation.

Scoring Guide for Report of Information Writing

	6-5 A-B range	4-3 points C range	2 D range	1
Effectiveness	Specific, concrete, detailed, relevant information throughout essay.	More general than specific information but includes details. Information selected as in 6-5 paper.	General statements. Uses lists without much development.	Off the subject
Fluency, Organization, Vocabulary	Essay has a controlling idea that unites and focuses. Strong introduction and conclusion. Effective transitions. Fresh descriptive and mature vocabulary.	Stays on topic but lacks focus. Weak introduction and conclusion. Some variety in vocabulary but may use cliches.	Only simple statement of the subject. Poorly organized or too little content to organize. Limited vocabulary.	
Mechanics	Capitalization, punctuation consistently done correctly. Rarely makes spelling errors.	Capitalization, punctuation consistently done correctly. May misspell difficult words.	Few correct uses of capitalization; limited use of appropriate punctuation. Frequent spelling errors of common words.	
Format	Title, margins, indentations done properly. Neatly written in ink or typed.	Title, margins, indentations done properly. Neatly written in ink or typed.	Title, margins, indentations done properly. Paper may be messy and written in pencil.	

Sleep Matters

Writing Situation

There is nothing like a good night's sleep to refresh us when we are tired. Yet sleep remains a mysterious phenomenon, and its relationship to health has not yet been fully explained. Researchers, however, have uncovered a great deal of information about what takes place during sleep, what disturbs sleep, and how to improve sleeping habits.

Writing Directions

Using the questionnaire your teacher will give you, conduct a survey of ten people to find out what they believe concerning sleep and its effect on health. Write a report for your science teacher explaining your findings. Include answers to the following questions: *What questions were generally answered correctly? What questions were generally answered incorrectly? How could knowing this information be helpful in changing attitudes or behavior?* Conclude your report by stating the insights you gained from conducting this survey.

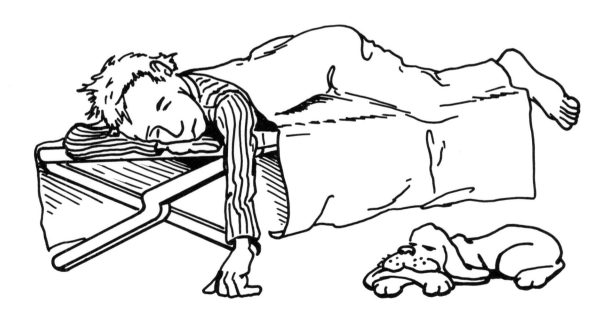

Sleep Matters
Sleeping Questionnaire

Use this questionnaire to conduct a survey of at least ten people. Ask the people you interview to tell whether each question is true or false, using the space to mark their answers. Record the correct answer to each question in the space before the question.

Correct answer

1._____Everyone needs eight hours of sleep a night.

2._____Insomnia affects only a small segment of the population.

3._____Sleeping pills are an effective, harmless way to deal with insomnia.

4._____Milk and certain other foods, taken before bedtime, help to put you to sleep.

5._____Sleep loss hinders your normal physical performance.

6._____Sleep loss hinders your normal mental performance.

7._____Poor sleep is a sign of poor health.

8._____Sleeping on a full stomach increases weight gain.

9._____You need to make up the exact amount of sleep you have lost.

Use this space to keep track of how many people answered the questions correctly and how many answered incorrectly.

	True	False			True	False
1.				2.		
3.				4.		
5.				6.		
7.				8.		
9.						

Sleep Matters
Information, Facts and Myths

Sleep is a highly organized series of events. It alternates between two phases: REM (rapid eye movement) and non-REM, both of which are necessary. A complete cycle of non-REM sleep followed by REM sleep averages 90 to 100 minutes and recurs four of five times during the night.

Non-REM sleep - This is the first phase, called quiet sleep. There is little or no body movement, brain activity is slow and regular and the five senses shut down. The non-REM phase passes through four stages as sleep gets progressively deeper, generally lasting a total of 70 to 90 minutes. The fourth and deepest stage, called delta sleep, is the most restorative.

REM sleep - This state of sleep is when dreams occur. It appears to be vital for psychological health. The eyes dart behind closed lids, heartbeat and metabolism speed up, and breathing, as well as brain waves, gets faster and more irregular. An average episode of REM lasts 10 to 20 minutes, but by the final cycle it can be 30 to 40 minutes long. During a typical eight-hour sleep 30 minutes to 2 hours is REM sleep.

Facts and Myths about Sleep and Health

1. **Myth: Everyone needs eight hours of sleep.**

   Fact: While the average person sleeps seven or eight hours, a good night's sleep is whatever leaves you feeling refreshed and alert the next day. This varies from person to person and with age. Some people need ten hours, others six.

2. **Myth: Poor sleep is a sign of poor health, particularly in an older person.**

   Fact: To a large extent, changes in sleep patterns are a natural part of the aging process and are nothing to worry about. Age is one of the most important factors affecting sleep. Infants can sleep 18 hours or more a day. By age 12 sleep patterns approximate those of adults. The next dramatic shift appears after age 60. Sleep becomes increasingly fragmented. We tend to wake up more often (and for longer periods) during the night, wake up earlier in the morning and sleep less deeply.

3. **Myth: Insomnia affects only a small segment of the population.**

   Fact: About 15% to 25% of all adults suffer regularly from insomnia (difficulty falling or staying asleep), and most of us have experienced it at one time or another. Insomnia is not a disorder but a symptom with many causes. Temporary insomnia can be caused, for instance, by jet lag or a stressful event.

4. **Myth**: **You need to make up the exact amount of sleep you have lost.**

   Fact: The body is remarkably efficient at making up for lost sleep. Studies have shown that even after being awake for days most people need only one long night's sleep to recover. People deprived of sleep make up for it by spending more time in the deep-sleep stage of the non-REM phase during subsequent nights.

5. **Myth: Sleeping pills are an effective and harmless way to deal with insomnia.**

   Fact: Sleeping pills may improve sleep temporarily but may be dangerous. Sleeping pills, called hypnotics, are among the most commonly taken drugs in the U.S., particularly among older people. These pills typically lead to further disruptions of sleep cycles — an increase in fragmented sleep, disturbing dreams and daytime fatigue. Increasing the dose only accustoms the body to a higher level of the drug and enhances the risk of side effects, addiction and overdosing.

6. **Myth**: **Warm milk and certain other foods help put you to sleep.**

   Fact: No food eaten at bedtime will guarantee a good night's sleep. What you eat has some chemical connection with sleep quality but the connection is not well understood. Attempts to treat sleep disorders through diet alone have had inconclusive results.

7. **Myth: Sleeping with a full stomach increases weight gain.**

   Fact: There is no evidence that calories consumed at night are stored more easily as fat than those taken in during the day. Assuming you eat the same foods and have the same activity level, it does not matter what time you eat. The calories you consume at night will simply be burned when needed.

8. **Myth: Sleep loss impairs normal physical performance**.

   Fact: Simple physical exertion is not significantly impaired by sleep loss. Studies have looked at subjects who stayed awake for 30 to 50 hours and then walked or cycled. Physical exertion was not altered by the sleep loss; however, subjects perceived that their exertion was greater than after a period of normal sleep. On the other hand, complex physical activities (such as playing tennis or baseball) that require vigilance or cognitive skills may be more difficult for a sleep-deprived person than repetitive activities such as running or swimming.

9. **Myth: Sleep loss impairs mental performance.**

   Fact: Since the most important benefit of sleep may be that it restores us mentally, our minds seem to suffer more from sleep loss than our bodies. A person kept up for long hours will generally feel fatigued and irritable, their attention span wanders, and they may experience mood shifts. The effect on mental ability depends on the type of thinking involved and amount of sleep lost.

Sleep Matters
Pre-composing Sheet

Use this sheet to organize the ideas you will be writing about. Choose the three most frequently missed questions. Then tell why the information is important or how knowing the correct answer to this question would be helpful in changing attitudes or behaviors.

Question _____ _____

_____

_____

Question _____ _____

_____

_____

Question _____ _____

_____

_____

What conclusions can you draw from this information? _____

_____

_____

What insights did you gain from conducting this survey? _____

_____

_____

Sleep Matters
Format

Use the following guidelines to organize your report about sleep and the results of your survey on knowledge of sleep information.

Paragraph 1 - Engage the interest of the reader by telling an anecdote, giving a definition or making a general statement about sleep.

Paragraph 2 - Explain the survey — how many people were interviewed, what type of questions were asked and why the survey was done.

Paragraph 3 - Choose any one of the most frequently missed questions to write about. Discuss how many people knew the correct answer, provide factual information related to the question, and explain the significance of knowing the correct answer and how the information could be helpful in changing attitudes or behaviors.

Paragraphs 4 and 5 - Do the same for the fourth and fifth paragraphs, using information from different questions.

Paragraph 6 - Sum up in a general statement the results of the survey. Tell what you learned from conducting this survey.

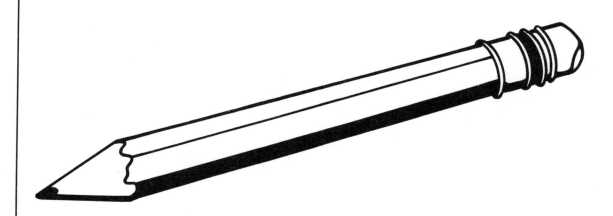

Why Math?

Writing Situation

A remark sometimes heard among students in school is that math is dull and useless. Seldom do we stop to think about how much we use mathematics every day of our lives or just how important it is to us. If you think about it, you will realize that not only is math a vital element in science and business, but everyone uses math in many different ways every day. Math has a variety of everyday applications and uses. Without an understanding of our number system and math, we would be severely limited in what we could do and how we could organize things.

Writing Directions

Write an essay for your teacher in which you discuss several ways you use mathematics in your daily life. Be specific and support your statements with good examples. Include an introduction, thesis statement and a conclusion.

Arithmetic

By Carl Sandburg

Arithmetic is where numbers fly like pigeons in and out of your head.

Arithmetic tells you how many you lose or win if you know how many you had before you lost or won.

Arithmetic is seven eleven all good children go to heaven — or five six bundle of sticks.

Arithmetic is numbers you squeeze from your head to your hand to your pencil to your paper till you get the answer.

Arithmetic is where the answer is right and everything is nice and you can look out of the window and see the blue sky — or the answer is wrong and you have to start all over and try again and see how it comes out this time.

If you take a number and double it and double it again and then double it a few more times, the number gets bigger and bigger and goes higher and higher and only arithmetic can tell you what the number is when you decide to quit doubling.

Arithmetic is where you have to multiply — and you carry the multiplication table in your head and hope you won't lose it.

If you have two animal crackers, one good and one bad, and you eat one and a striped zebra with streaks all over him eats the other, how many animal crackers will you have if somebody offers you five six seven and you say No no no and you say Nay nay nay and you say Nix nix nix?

If you ask your mother for one fried egg for breakfast and she gives you two fried eggs and you eat both of them, who is better in arithmetic, you or your mother?

Why Math?

A Morning Filled with Numbers

This page describes a typical morning of someone your age. As you read it, be aware of all the different ways math plays a part in this student's life. Be thinking of other ways that you use math in your life.

The alarm clock shatters the beautiful dream you are having. Drowsily, you open one blurry eye and peer at the lighted numeral of the clock; it's 6:20 A.M. With one hand, you squelch the obnoxious sound and mumble to yourself, "Fifteen minutes more won't matter." Half conscious, you remember that if you're late one more day to school, you'll have to serve detention. You mentally and physically force your body out of bed, one foot on the cold floor, then the next. Stumbling to the thermostat, you move the dial to 72 degrees and head for the shower.

Slightly revived, you dress quickly and automatically move toward the kitchen. Glancing at the kitchen clock, you see that fifteen minutes has elapsed. Still enough time for some hot cereal, you muse to yourself. Carefully you measure one cup of hot water, pour it in a pan with a little salt, and switch on the stove. Next, you measure one quarter cup of oatmeal. While you wait for the water to boil, you flip on the radio just in time to hear the weather report, "Eighty percent chance of rain today." "Oh great," you think to yourself, "and I have to ride my bike three miles to school." Music follows the weather. The water in the pan is now bubbling. You stir in the oatmeal, setting the timer on the stove for two minutes. Glancing at the counter, you see your mom has left you $2.00 lunch money.

While you pour the oatmeal in a bowl, you think about what you can buy with the $2.00. "Let's see, I could spend 40 cents for a snack and still have $1.60 for lunch," you think. While you pour milk and sugar on your cereal, you calculate 80 cents for a hamburger, 40 cents for fries, and 40 cents for a drink. Not bad!

You grab your coat, hat and books and dash out the door. You jump on your bike as the first sprinkles of rain hit your nose. "What's the shortest route to school?" you ask yourself, not wanting to be drenched by the time you arrive. Mentally you figure the short cuts and take off. Finally, you reach school, park your bike and dash to your locker. Fortunately, the rain seems to be stopping. Glancing at your watch, you see you have five minutes left. Quickly, you spin the combination, right 22, left 19, right 6, and left 2. It opens and you grab your math book and head for class, just as the bell rings.

Sliding into your seat, you finally relax. Looking around the room, you see mostly girls. You've never noticed that before. You wonder what the ratio of boys to girls is at this school. "Please turn to page 98," the teacher announces. "Math," you say to yourself. "How will I ever use this stuff anyway?"

Why Math?
Pre-composing Sheet

1. Under each category list as many ways as you can to show how mathematics is used in your daily life.

Time _____

_____

Measurement _____

_____

Recreational activities _____

_____

Money _____

_____

Science _____

_____

Art _____

_____

Architecture _____

_____

Industry _____

_____

2. Choose three of the areas listed above to write about. List your choices here.

   a._____ b._____ c._____

3. Complete the following sentence to use as your thesis statement:

   Everyday I use math in_____ , _____ , and _____ .

Why Math?
Format

Use the following guidelines to organize your essay about how you use math everyday.

Paragraph 1 - This is your introductory paragraph that states the things you will be writing about in your essay. Begin by making a general statement about how we use math daily. The last sentence in this paragraph should be your thesis statement.

Paragraph 2 - Write a topic sentence introducing your first main point. Write only about the first point you mention in your thesis statement. Give examples to support your ideas.

Paragraph 3 - Write a topic sentence introducing your second main point. Give examples to support the importance of math in this area of life.

Paragraph 4 - Introduce your third main point. Expand on the topic sentence with examples from real life.

Paragraph 5 - Conclusion. Restate the thesis statement and make a concluding statement.

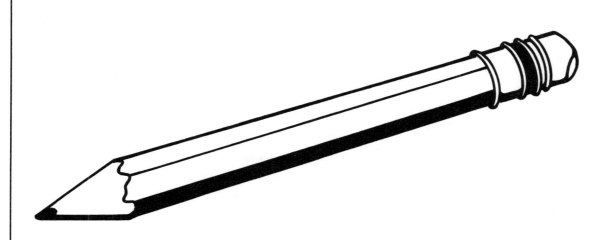

Dear Diary

Writing Situation

In the book and play, *The Diary of Anne Frank*, Anne Frank, her family and some friends had to go into hiding to avoid persecution from the Germans during World War II. They were in hiding for one and a half years. During that time they had to remain absolutely quiet during the day and they could never go outside their cramped quarters. They could never even have the luxury of walking down the street in the bright sunshine. What would it be like if you had to live under these circumstances?

Directions for Writing

Write an essay for your English teacher in which you describe the things you would miss the most if you were in Anne's place and were forced to stay inside. To do this you must first think about your current daily activities. Then decide which ones would be impossible to do in hiding. You will also want to think about the friends and pets you would miss. Try to be very specific and include descriptions of your feelings.

Dear Diary

Free to Be
By Beryl Bennett

The wind in the trees is calling to me,
"Come Out! Come Out! Set yourself free."

Free to run to your heart's content
Step, after step, 'till all energy's spent.

Free to walk in the winter rain,
Splashing in puddles, along every lane.

Free to lie on the soft beach sand,
Drowsily dreaming of distant lands.

Free to sit with friends and plan,
All of the fun things that you can.

Free to ride on the back of a horse,
Flying through space, along any course.

The wind in the trees is calling to me.
"Come out! Come Out! Be free, like me."

Dear Diary
Pre-composing Sheet

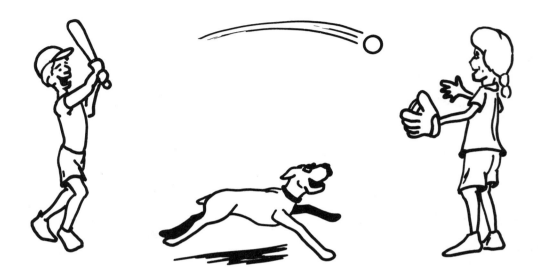

Use this outline to help you organize your thoughts about what it would be like to be in Anne Frank's place. Fill in the outline with as many examples as you can.

1. Activities I enjoy outside _____

_____

2. Activities I enjoy with my friends _____

_____

3. Places I like to visit _____

_____

4. Special people I would miss _____

_____

5. Pets and animals I would miss _____

_____

6. Other things I would miss _____

_____

Dear Diary
Format

Use the following guidelines to organize your essay about what it would be like to be in Anne Frank's place.

Paragraph 1 - Introduction. In this paragraph describe Anne Frank's situation. Develop a thesis statement. It might say something like, "If I were forced to stay inside as Anne was, I would miss many activities."

Paragraph 2 - Write about the activities you enjoy doing outside that you would miss.

Paragraph 3 - Write about the friends you would miss and the activities you do with them.

Paragraph 4 - Write about the special people and pets you would miss.

Paragraph 5 - Conclude your essay with a sentence or two that describes your feelings about being free to do the things you wish to do. Give your essay a feeling of finality.

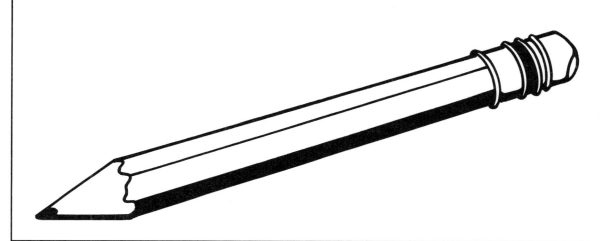

Lifestyles

Writing Situation

Lifestyles have changed throughout history. A young person living in Colonial times or during the Revolutionary era would live differently and engage in activities quite unlike those you engage in today. Education, home life, dress, entertainment and hobbies would all be different today compared to an earlier period in our history.

Directions for Writing

What is your lifestyle like today? Write a letter to an imaginary person from an earlier period in history. In this letter tell what life today is like for a person your age. You may wish to include information about your school, hobbies, family or favorite pastimes. Include examples, facts, details and explanations. Remember you are writing to a person your own age.

Lifestyles in the Colonial Period

The following imaginary diary entries might help you compare your lifestyle with that of a young person living in the United States during the Colonial Period.

Home

After school we have to help our parents by doing chores at home. Each afternoon, we have many chores to do. Girls help with candle making, cooking and sewing. Boys help tend the animals, work in the fields and do carpentry work.

Frontier Hunting Games

I can imitate the noise of every bird or beast in the woods. By gobbling, I attract wild turkeys to come within reach of my rifle. I also like to play "throwing the tomahawk."

School

My father taught me to read before I went to school. Now that I am in school, I have to study Latin, which I find difficult. Sometimes I leave class and go hunting in the woods. We also learn from a book called *The School of Good Manners*. This book tells us to use a title of respect, such as sir or madam, when we speak to our parents. It tells us to live in love, peace and unity and to bear our parents' corrections with meekness and patience. The other subjects taught in our school include religion, reading, writing, arithmetic, history and geography. Some of my friends are taught at home, and some learn a job skill at home or at a place of business. We usually go to school from eight in the morning until one in the afternoon. Before we go home, we sing some verses and a psalm from the Bible.

Games

We enjoy playing musical chairs with our parents or friends. Most of our toys are made from everyday objects such as old stockings and corncobs. Father carved a spinning top for me and made a wooden rocking horse for my little brother. When it is warm, we play lawn bowling. My friends and I also like to see who can keep a hoop rolling the longest. We love to tell and listen to stories. Sometimes the stories become very tall tales and are funny.

Lifestyles
Pre-composing Sheet

Think about your lifestyle. Under each category below, write down ideas that describe your particular situation. Be as specific and descriptive as possible.

1. Home and family

_____

_____

_____

2. School

_____

_____

_____

3. Entertainment, hobbies or sports

_____

_____

_____

4. Clothing

_____

_____

_____

Lifestyles
Format

Use the format for a friendly letter for your writing assignment. Include the date, a salutation, and a closing that would be appropriate for this type of letter. The body of your letter should include the following information.

Date

Dear (name of imaginary friend),

Paragraph 1 - Introduce the subject of your letter and tell what aspects of your lifestyle you will discuss.

Paragraph 2 - Tell about one of your choices. For example, write about your home.

Paragraph 3 - Write about another choice; school, for example.

Paragraph 4 - Share information about another area of your lifestyle, perhaps sports, entertainment, hobbies or activities.

Paragraph 5 - Tell about another choice, perhaps the clothing you wear.

Paragraph 6 - Close your letter with a paragraph that summarizes the things you have discussed and gives the reader a sense of finality.

Yours truly,
Your Name

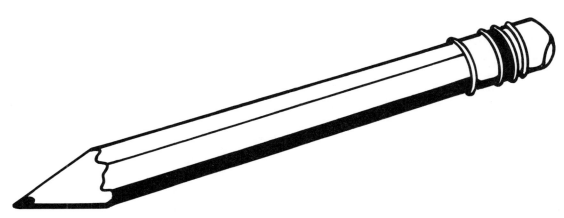

A Favorite Color

Writing Situation

Imagine a world without color! Imagine roses not being red, the grass not being green and the dandelions of summer not being a gleaming yellow. Fortunately we live in a world bathed in color. Even though we have a multitude of beautiful colors all around us that we enjoy, we usually have one color that is our favorite.

Writing Directions

What is your favorite color? Describe it in an essay for your teacher. Tell how your favorite color affects your senses and feelings and how it reflects your personality and mood. Include cliches, sayings or proverbs that use your color and any other word associations it brings to mind. Use your imagination and make your report colorful.

68

Color Connotations

These pages will give you information about what effect different colors typically have on people. You can use this information about colors to help you start thinking about your favorite color and what the color means to you and to other people.

Black

Black often symbolizes death. It is often associated with negative images; *blacklist, blackmail, black-ball, black market,* or *black sheep*. In the United States teenagers from beatniks through rockers and punks, have adopted black as a negative symbol showing they reject society's values. But black can also represent the ultimate in sophistication and quality.

White

White is associated with purity; therefore, a popular color for brides. It also represents cleanliness. White is also a symbol for surrender, as in waving a white flag. Some expressions that refer to the color white are *white lie, white magic, white flag,* and *white wash.*

Red

Red is thought to be the first color perceived by babies. It is an impulsive color, attractive to people who value things that offer intensity of living and fullness of experience. It represents vitality, power, excitement and courage. It is equated with the heart, flesh and emotion. It denotes joy and happiness. Some expressions containing the word red are *red hot, red carpet, red cent, red tape, red-letter day,* and *seeing red.*

Pink

Pink is a feminine color, often associated with babies. Among Medieval color terms, pink described flights of fancy. It suggests tip-top condition and high spirits. If you are in the pink everything is rosy. You can also look through rose colored glasses, which means that you see the good side of things.

Orange

Orange is an earth color. If autumn has a color, it is orange. Orange has exotic overtones because it is a common color for spices. Because it is so highly visible, it is used for road signs and signals at sea. Orange is associated with tension and with energy.

Yellow

Yellow is associated with two important elements in human history: the life-giving sun and gold, the measure of earthly wealth. It is said to represent intellect. It radiates warmth, inspiration and a sunny disposition and is the characteristic color of spring. Some expressions that refer to the color yellow are *yellow streak*, *yellow journalism*, *yellow-bellied*, and *golden age* or *golden opportunity*.

Green

Green is the color of foliage, of rebirth. Green is the most restful color to the eyes and is associated with the qualities of stability and security. Green is also the color of creepiness, reminding us of slithery creatures like frogs, snakes, lizards, dragons and science fiction monsters. A few of its other associations are camouflage, being inexperienced or gullible, good gardeners and money.

Blue

Blue has a historic and symbolic association with royalty. In clothing, the color flatters nearly everyone. It is associated with the qualities of a peacemaker; cool, soothing and orderly. Sadness and depression are often described as being blue, but blue skies are a cure for the blues. Blue is a synonym for the best — the blue ribbon. Associated with work, peace and contentment, blue is a passive and tranquil color. Some expressions that contain the word blue are *feeling blue, blue moon, blue ribbon, blue blood, out of the blue* and *Blues* (music).

Purple or Violet

Because purple dye was prized in the ancient world, the color purple was a symbol of luxury and royalty. It was also associated with magic. In psychology, violet is associated with depth of feeling. The purple gem, amethyst, was a love charm, an aid to sleep and protection against thieves.

For an additional resource, read *Hailstones, and Halibut Bones, Adventures in Color* by Mary Leduc O'Neill.

Favorite Color
Pre-composing Sheet

Write down as many ideas as you can to answer the following questions about your favorite color. Continue on the back of this sheet or another piece of paper if you need more room.

My favorite color is _____

1. The senses

How does your color make you feel? Explain why. _____

If your color could, would it shout, scream, whisper, speak gently or speak in some other way? _____

What flavor is your color and how would it taste? _____

What kind of music do you associate with your color and why? _____

2. Reflections

How does your color reflect your personality? Why? Your mood? Why? _____

In nature, what is the same color as your favorite color? _____

What do you own that is your favorite color? _____

If you could, how would you add more of your favorite color to the world? _____

3. Associations

List all the things you can that are the same color as your favorite color._____

List any sayings, cliches or proverbs that use your color. _____

Is your color associated with a personality trait or behavior? _____

Favorite Color
Format

Use the following guidelines to organize your essay about color.

Paragraph 1 - This is your introductory paragraph. Engage the reader's interest in your subject. State the thesis — for example, "Ever since I was a small child, I have loved the color blue."

Paragraph 2 - Write about how your color affects your senses.

Paragraph 3 - Write about how your color reflects your personality, mood, things in the world, and things in nature.

Paragraph 4 - Write about the connotations, expressions, cliches, or proverbs associated with your color.

Paragraph 5 - In your conclusion, sum up the main ideas and let the reader know that you have come to the end of your essay.

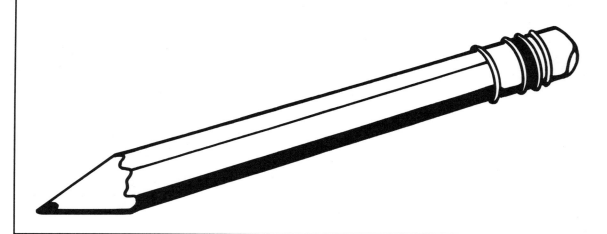

Preparing for a Natural Disaster

On Tuesday, October 17, 1989, the San Francisco Bay Area was rocked by a severe earthquake. The total costs in loss of life and property were monumental. Some feel the residents of the area were as prepared as possible; others disagree. Although we cannot be as prepared for an earthquake or other natural disaster as we may like to be, there are certain things we can do.

Write a report for your science teacher describing the things you could do at home and at school to be as prepared as possible for an earthquake or some other natural disaster. Be specific and describe how each thing would be useful.

Staying Healthy

The traits you inherited from your parents affect how healthy you are. But you, yourself, have a lot more to do with how healthy you are. What are some things you can do to try to ensure good health?

Write a report for your science teacher describing the things people can do to stay healthy. Be sure to include preventative and protective measures.

Your Wonderful Body

The human body is a wonderful thing. Its beauty lies in each individual cell and also in the powerful systems these cells create. Amazingly each cell and each system does its part and reacts to other systems, making the human body the most intricate, well-designed and incredible machine that has ever been produced.

Write an essay in which you tell why the human body is an incredible machine. Share specific information that supports your general statements regarding why the human body is special.

Polling People

People are often curious about the likes and dislikes of other people. There are even companies whose express purpose is finding out peoples' opinions and favorite things. To do this they conduct a poll, contacting people and asking them how they feel about things.

Decide on several topics that are of interest to you. These could include things such as favorite music or musical group, favorite type of jeans, sport or ice cream. Take a poll of about 25 people. Write a report for your school newspaper disclosing the results. Include a good introduction and conclusion. Try to keep your report unbiased.

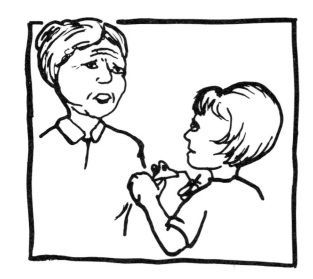

What is an Abacus?

The abacus is a calculating device that has been around for a long time. It is simple in design, consisting of a frame with moveable counters on parallel rods or grooves; yet it can help a person do complicated mathematical problems.

Research the abacus and write a report about it. Describe how the abacus works, how it was developed, and how long it has been used.

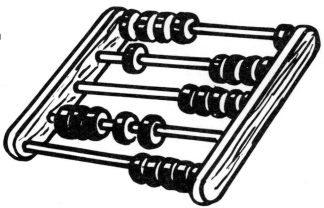

Mighty Mathematicians

Through the years many people have made important contributions to the field of mathematics. Learning about these people can be very interesting and can help you gain insight not only into the development of mathematical concepts, but also into the way mathematics is related to history, geography, and economics.

In the library research a famous mathematician. Write a report describing the life of this person and the contributions made to the study of mathematics.

$$E = MC^2$$

Describing Your School

Receiving a letter from a friend is always a satisfying experience, and knowing the proper form of the friendly letter will help you throughout life as you correspond with friends and family.

A friend of one of your cousins is moving to your area and will be attending your school. His name is Tom Smith, and he is in the same grade as you are. You have never met this boy, but he has written to you wanting to know what he can expect when he attends your school. He will be interested in information about classes, teachers, schedules, students, extra curricular activities, rules, and attitudes. Be friendly and helpful in your reply.

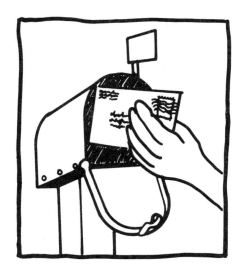

Words of Wisdom

Many proverbs and quotes have survived historically because they address issues that are always appropriate and meaningful. The following quote from the Renaissance period is one example: "The value of life lies not in the length of days but in the use we make of them." (Montaigne)

Write an essay for your English teacher discussing this quotation. Restate the quote in your own words. Cite examples from your own life in which you manage your time in certain ways in order to accomplish certain tasks. Compare and contrast this quotation with the popular proverb, "The early bird gets the worm."

Change of Character

In Pearl Buck's *The Good Earth*, Wang Lung, the main character, changes from a poor farmer to a wealthy land owner. In the process, his personalty and actions also change drastically.

Write a report for your English teacher describing the ways a character changed in a novel you have read recently. Describe what caused the changes. Use specific examples to describe the character at the beginning and at the end of the novel. Comment on whether you think the changes were good or bad.

Hero

Webster's dictionary defines a hero as "someone exhibiting or marked by courage and daring" and also "of impressive size, power or effect." Throughout history there have been men and women whom we have revered because of their heroic qualities.

Write an essay for your social studies teacher in which you describe what, in your opinion, makes a hero. Explain the specific qualities required. Tell what kind of acts would be considered heroic to you. Cite some examples of people from history whose lives exemplify your definition of a hero.

Barter and Trade

Before the development of money people bartered or traded with their neighbors for the things they needed. Now most sales are conducted in stores and money is used to pay for the goods and services we desire.

Think about how your life would change if you could only barter or trade for the things that you needed or wanted. Write an essay for your social studies teacher explaining the differences that would occur with this kind of economy. Think about specific things you use daily and describe how you might acquire them. Tell why you think this system would be better or worse than what we have now.

Melting Pot

The United States is known as a great "melting pot." Do some research in the library about the immigration to the United States in the 1900s. Find out why this country came to be called a "melting pot."

Write a report for your social studies teacher explaining why immigrants came to this country in the 1900s, from what countries they came and for what reasons. Also explain how they arrived and how they were treated when they got here. Explain how the poem printed at the base of the Statue of Liberty relates to immigration.

Art Everywhere

Examples of art can be found everywhere. The colors and designs in our clothing reflect elements of art. Our homes are decorated to suit our tastes in an artful way. Looking around us, we see buildings, pictures and signs designed by artists and architects. We often take the created art around us for granted.

Write an essay for your school newspaper entitled, "In Appreciation of Art." Give some examples of the art surrounding you and explain how it enhances your life. Try to lead other students to a greater appreciation for the art around them.

Giving Directions

You have completed several projects in your art class. Your teacher helped and directed you along the way. Would you, in turn, be able to tell a friend exactly how to make one of the projects?

Your friend wants to make a project like yours. In report form tell your friend how to do it. Begin by listing all the materials needed. Describe each step of the process thoroughly and sequentially. End your report with a description of what the completed project should look like.

Working with Clay

Working with clay can be fun, but one must learn certain techniques beforehand to be successful.

Write a report to be read to your craft class. Describe the basic things every student should know before working with clay. Include how to prepare the clay, care for it, dry, fire and glaze it. Describe how to make a slip and join clay parts.

Student Response Guide
Checking for Content

Evaluator _____

Author of paper _____

Title of the paper _____

This page will help your partner make sure all the elements of report of information writing has been included. It will help him/her determine what should be added, changed or deleted. If you cannot answer a question, leave it blank. Your partner will know that he/she needs to clarify this point more thoroughly.

1. Does the beginning capture the reader's interest?

2. What is the thesis statement or controlling idea of this paper?

3. Briefly list the main points made in this paper.

4. Are there details, facts, examples or explanations to support the main points? What are they?

5. Copy any details, facts or examples that do not relate to the topic.

6. How does the writer organize this writing? Check appropriate way:

   _____chronologically (order of time)   _____categorically (grouping by subject)   _____other

7. Is the writing well organized?

8. Can you tell how the writer feels about this subject? If so, briefly explain how he/ she feels.

9. Did the writer give you enough information to inform you about the subject?

10. Copy any words or phrases that you think should have been explained but were not.

11. Did the paper have a good conclusion that summed up the main ideas?

Writing Checklist
Checking the Mechanics

Evaluator _____

Author of paper _____

Title of paper _____

This page will help your partner correct spelling errors, paragraphing, punctuation and grammar. In addition to answering the questions, your teacher may want you to use a colored pen to circle the errors on your partner's paper.

yes or no

1._____Every sentence begins with a capital letter.

2._____There is end punctuation for every sentence.

3._____Paragraphing is correctly done.

4._____Spelling has been checked (circle misspelled words).

5._____Run-on and sentence fragments have been checked.

6._____Sentences do not begin with "and", "so" or "so then".

7._____The title and all proper nouns are capitalized.

8._____Correct punctuation (commas, contractions, etc.) is used.

9._____Subjects and verbs agree in number.

10._____The author "shows" instead of just telling.

Comments

I especially like this about your paper. _____

_____

These things are still unclear to me. _____

_____

Works Cited

The Architectural Digest Book, Color. New York: The Viking Press, 1980.

The Earth Group. *Fifty Simple Things You Can Do To Save The Earth.* Berkeley, CA: EarthWorks Press, 1989.

O'Neill, Mary Leduc. *Hailstones and Halibut Bones, Adventures in Color.* New York: Doubleday and Company Inc., 1961.

Sandburg, Carl. "Arithmetic", *The Complete Poems of Carl Sandburg.* San Diego, CA: Harcourt Brace World Inc., 1950.

Schlissel, Lillian. *Women's Diaries of the Westward Journey.* New York: Schocken Books, 1982.

Other Books from **Dandy Lion** that build skills and knowledge in the area of language or writing include:

Alphabet Soup

Investigator

Sketch and Scribe

Speaker's Club

Writing Lab

Writing Winning Reports

Look for other quality products from **Dandy Lion** in the areas of creativity, imagery, interpersonal and personal skills, research and independent study, literature and reading, logic and thinking skills, mathematics, science, and general enrichment. Your will find these products at your educational supply store, or you may call or write for a catalog that lists our complete line of products.

ISBN 0-931724-77-5

50895

9 780931 724770

DANDY LION